This book belongs to

....

....

This edition published by Parragon Books Ltd in 2015

Parragon Books Ltd
Chartist House
15–17 Trim Street
Bath BA1 1HA, UK
www.parragon.com

ISBN 978-1-4723-4934-7

Printed in China

Disney · PIXAR

THE GOOD DINOSAUR

Book of Bravery

PaRragon

Bath · New York · Cologne · Melbourne · Delhi
Hong Kong · Shenzhen · Singapore · Amsterdam

In a world where dinosaurs became farmers instead of extinct, there lived two Apatosauruses called Henry and Ida. They loved each other very much and decided to start a family.

Henry and Ida had three children — Buck, Libby and Arlo. Arlo was the youngest and afraid of everything! Most of all, Arlo was afraid of the wilderness beyond the family's farm.

One night, Henry took Arlo into the field. Suddenly, an insect landed on Arlo's nose. Arlo was scared, but Poppa blew gently on the insect — and it glowed!

Then Poppa swept his tail through the grass, and hundreds of fireflies flew into the sky. Arlo was amazed.

The next day, Poppa discovered a critter eating their food.
"You're gonna catch that critter!" he told Arlo.
Arlo was afraid, but he wanted to make his Poppa proud.
As Arlo guarded the silo, he heard something get caught in
Poppa's trap. That's when he got his first look at the critter — it
was a human boy! Arlo didn't want to harm him, so he let him go.

Henry wasn't pleased when he saw the empty trap. He decided to teach his son a lesson by taking him into the wilderness to find the critter. But while they were gone, a terrifying storm caused the river to overflow and poor Poppa was swept away in a flood!

Arlo watched his Poppa disappear, horrified.

With Poppa gone, the family had to work very hard to keep the farm going. Arlo was determined to help take care of his family.

One day, Arlo caught the critter stealing corn again. As he and the critter fought, they tumbled backwards into the river.

"Momma!" Arlo cried, but he had been swept too far away for anyone to hear. The river carried Arlo away. Then — BAM! The little dinosaur hit his head on a rock and he was pulled under by the current.

When Arlo awoke, he had no idea where he was. He was alone and the wilderness was all around him. Suddenly, Arlo heard a howl. Standing on the clifftop above him was the critter.

"You!" shouted Arlo angrily. "This is all your fault!" Furious, he tried to climb up the cliff to get at the little boy. But the critter wasn't afraid.

The critter scampered off, leaving the dinosaur all alone. Arlo was scared, hungry and tired.

Before long it started to get dark, and Arlo felt raindrops on his head.

Arlo decided to build a shelter using twigs and branches. Once his shelter was complete, he curled up beneath its leaky roof and tried to sleep. But then he heard something rustling in the bushes outside, heading in his direction....

It was … the boy! He had brought Arlo a
branch of berries, and that's when the dinosaur
and the boy became friends.

Arlo gave the boy a name — Spot.

Spot couldn't talk, but he and Arlo found a
way of communicating.

Arlo learned that Spot had lost his family,
just as the dinosaur had lost his Poppa.

A few days later, Arlo and Spot met a family of T. rexes called Butch, Ramsey and Nash. They had lost their herd of longhorns.

Arlo offered to help the T. rexes if they could show him the way home. Butch agreed, and Spot tracked down the longhorns. But a nasty surprise lay in wait....

Raptors! This gang of feathery crooks had stolen the longhorns, and weren't going to give them up without a fight. Brave Arlo helped his new friends.

"You're one tough kid," Butch told Arlo.

As promised, the T. rexes helped Arlo and Spot find the direction home, and the pair continued on their journey.

Spot climbed atop Arlo's head and pointed towards the sky. Above the clouds was the most beautiful sunset they had ever seen.

As Arlo and Spot made their way along the mountain pass, a storm was brewing.

Suddenly, a pack of Pterodactyls swooped down and caught hold of Spot and whisked him up and away!

Arlo gave chase and found Spot down by the river. Arlo felt a surge of courage in his heart and charged at the Pterodactyls, driving them away.

The storm was raging now, and suddenly the river burst its banks! Arlo and Spot were swept away in the flood. The dinosaur could see his friend, but he couldn't reach him. Arlo reached Spot just as they tumbled over a waterfall.

The two friends clung to each other as they fell into the river far, far below.
Arlo climbed ashore holding his friend.
They were okay.

Arlo and Spot set off once again.
Suddenly, they heard a howl and
a human family appeared.

Arlo knew what he had to do. Even though he didn't want to lose Spot, he let him go. The two friends cried as they said goodbye.

Arlo carried on alone and, before long, he saw something that made him very happy — the farm!

At last, Arlo was home.

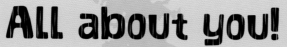

All about you!

Arlo is the youngest member of a family of Apatosauruses. He loves his life on the farm, where his Poppa and Momma work hard to look after their three children.

Let's learn about you!

Name: ....

Birthday: ....

Hair colour: ....

Height: ....

Stick a photo of
yourself here!

Meet the Family!

Arlo belongs to a loving family. His Poppa is devoted to the farm and family, and his Momma looks after everyone. Arlo also has a sister called Libby, and a brother called Buck.

HENRY – Poppa

IDA – Momma

LIBBY – Big Sister

ARLO – Little Brother

BUCK – Big Brother

Now draw your own family below.
Don't forget to write down who's who!

A day out

Poppa takes Arlo into a field on the farm to show him the fireflies. At first, Arlo is scared of the insects — but then Poppa shows him how to make the bugs glow! Write about a fun family outing that you enjoyed.

One day, my family went to ....

....

....

....

....

....

....

....

....

....

Sometimes it's a good idea to write down your thoughts about your family. You might discover things you never knew!

Who makes me laugh the most? ....

....

....

Who spends the most time with me? ....

....

....

Who am I most like? ....

....

Who gives the best hugs? ....

....

Me and my friend

Arlo's best friend is Spot – but who is yours? Draw a picture of your friend in the space below. Then write down your three favourite things about them on the opposite page.

.... is my best friend because...

1. ....

....

☐

2. ....

....

☐

3. ....

....

☐

Can you pick your top favourite thing about your friend?
Tick the box next to the one you think is most important.

Pet collector

Arlo meets many strange characters on his adventure through the wilderness. One of them, called Forrest Woodbush, collects different kinds of animals. Write about your own pets here.

Name: ....

Nickname: ....

Type of animal: ....

Favourite food: ....

Best thing about them: ....

....

....

If you don't have any pets, make some up! Let your imagination run wild!

Name: ....

Nickname: ....

Type of animal: ....

Favourite food: ....

Best thing about them: ....

....

....

Name: ....

Nickname: ....

Type of animal: ....

Favourite food: ....

Best thing about them: ....

....

....

Into the Wild!

Arlo was scared of the wilderness beyond his farm, but then he went on an incredible journey. It taught him there are all kinds of places in the world. If you could go on a wild adventure, where would you go? Draw a map of your imaginary trip!

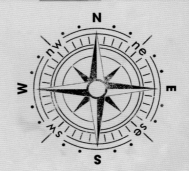

Places you could include:

Mountains, rivers, marshlands, volcanoes, forests, plains, farms, towns, oceans, caves, and anything else you can think of!

Dinosaurs rule!

How much do you love dinosaurs? Tick the footprint next to your favourite dinosaur.

Apatosaurus

Tyrannosaurus

Velociraptor

Styracosaurus

Dino decider

Arlo is an Apatosaurus. What kind of dinosaur would you be? Take the test and find out, then draw the result on the opposite page!

I am...

1. Kind   2. Tough   3. Mean

I get around on...

1. All fours   2. Two legs   3. Wings

If I see a helpless creature, I will...

1. Help it   2. Ignore it   3. Eat it

I mostly eat...

1. Berries   2. Crocodiles   3. Anything

My favourite thing in the world is...

1. Family ☐   2. Fighting ☐   3. Storms ☐

How did you do?

Mostly 1s

You're an
Apatosaurus!

Mostly 2s

You're a
T. rex!

Mostly 3s

You're a
Pterodactyl!

Draw your dino here!

Family album

Family is very important to Arlo. When he gets lost in the wilderness he has to close his eyes to picture the faces of his loved ones. Stick photographs of your family members in this album.

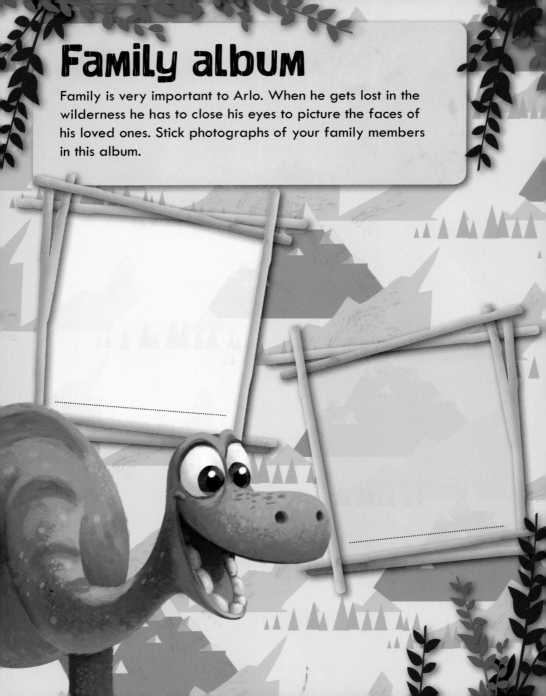

Home sweet home

When Arlo gets lost in the wilderness, he thinks of home. Would you miss your home? Write about it below and draw a picture of your house on the next page.

Location: ....

House ☐   Flat ☐   Caravan ☐

Number of rooms: ....

Favourite room: ....

Favourite neighbour: ....

....

....

Draw your home here!

Your heroes

Arlo looks up to his Poppa as a hero. Who are your heroes? Write about your real-life sports, school, family and film heroes here.

My sports hero

Name: ....

My hero because: ....

....

....

What I like best about them: ....

....

....

....

My school hero

Name: ....

My hero because: ....

....

....

What I like best about them: ....

....

....

....

My family hero

Name: ....

My hero because: ....
....
....

What I like best about them: ....
....
....
....

My film hero

Name: ....

My hero because: ....
....
....

What I like best about them: ....
....
....
....

Brave and bold

After feeling afraid all the time, Arlo realizes that he is brave when he stands up to some raptors. Write about a time that you felt brave and draw a picture of yourself on the opposite page.

Where were you?..
....

....

What did you do?...

....

....

....

Who was there?..

....

....